THE ADVENTURES OF SUMMER AND

I GOT A PUPPY!

by Summer Arrington,
Tatyana Arrington, Vanessa Arrington
illustrated by Courtney Monday

1

Manufactured in the United States of America

Cataloging-in-Publication data for this book is available from the Library of Congress

ISBN: 978-1-7352637-7-9

Illustrator: Courtney Monday

USA $ 15.99

This book is dedicated to
Ahjanee "Lemon" Arrington

Special thank you to our
Family, Friends, and all Dog
Lovers.

Thank you to our Dad, Ken for bringing Winter into our family.

Thank you to Dr. Adair White-Johnson for guiding us through the process of self-publishing.

Special thank you to our illustrator, Courtney Monday, for bringing our vision to life.

Hi! My name is Summer just like the season. What's your name?

_____

Today is a special day. It's my birthday and it is also the last day of school. I'm 5 years old. How old are you?

I love to eat pancakes for breakfast. Mmm they're delicious. Do you like pancakes?

8

I'm wearing my birthday outfit.
Do you like my dress? It's pink
which is my favorite color.

What's your favorite color?

I love school! We learn new things everyday and we play fun games.

Today is Show n Tell. I brought my
stuffed animal puppy. I love Puppies!
They are so soft and cute.
They are my favorite animals.

Do you have a favorite animal?

I can't wait to get home to celebrate my birthday with my family.

It's 2:15pm, time to go home!
Good-bye Mrs. Williams,
have a great Summer!

Wow! Look at the pretty
balloons and decorations!

18

I have so many presents. Can you count the number of presents?

My cake looks delicious! There are 5 candles on my cake and 1 candle for good luck. Chocolate cake is my favorite!

Happy Birthday Summer

I have one more present to open.
This box is filled with lots of holes. It's a
present from my Mommy and Daddy.

Surprise!!!

Arf!

A puppy is a big responsibility Summer. Responsibility means you have to take care of your puppy all of the time. Do you agree to do that?

Yes Mommy! What kind of puppy is it?

It's a Yorkie. You will have to walk the puppy twice a day, feed the puppy twice a day and train the puppy. Are you ready for that Summer?

30

Of course I am!

What should I name her?

I got it! I will name her Winter.
Winter is the opposite of Summer.
She's soft and fluffy just like snow.

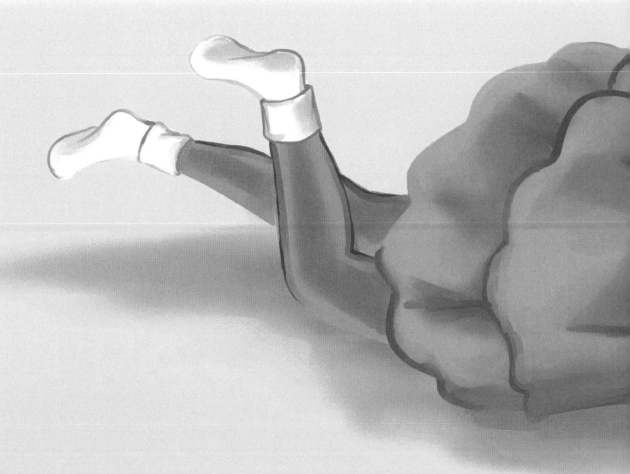

I love my puppy Winter!
We're going to have so much fun
together. A puppy is a responsibility.
I'm ready to be responsible.

C'mon Winter let me introduce you to my friends.

37

Surprise!!! "Happy Birthday Summer!!!"

Thanks friends, meet
my new puppy Winter.
Winter what do you
want to do first?

Arf!!!

40

Oh No Winter! It's almost time for dinner we have to go home!

42

Bye friends!

"How was your birthday with your new puppy Winter?"

Awesome! I think this is the start of an exciting adventure.

AUTHOR'S BIOS

Summer Arrington is a high school sophomore honor student who loves animals and has an enthusiasm for writing. She is a member of The National Beta Club, The National Honor Society, Technology Student Association, and Student Council. She also has a sincere passion for Dance and has dreams of becoming a professional dancer. Follow @theadventuresofsummerandwinter

Tatyana Arrington is an actress, entertainment reporter, and a social media influencer. She received her Bachelor's Degree in Communications with a concentration in Theatre from Georgia Southern University. She enjoys traveling, concerts, films, reading, and writing. Follow @xotatyana

Vanessa Arrington has a deep appreciation for the arts and earned a Bachelor's Degree in Communications from Oglethorpe University. She currently serves as a Senior Marketing Specialist in Urban Radio. She enjoys listening to music, reading, writing, sketching, and spending time with family and friends. Follow @veearrington

Made in the USA
Las Vegas, NV
13 April 2021